101 True Scary Stories to Read in Bed Tonight

101 True Scary Stories to Read in Bed Tonight

LANE LOOMIS

THOUGHT
CATALOG
Books

BROOKLYN, NY

Cover design by KJ Parish.

Published by Thought Catalog Books, a publishing house owned by The Thought & Expression Co., Williamsburg, Brooklyn.

First edition, 2017

ISBN: 978-1945796685

Printed and bound in the United States.

10 9 8 7 6 5 4 3 2 1

Contents

Introduction

We've all heard the story of the call that comes from inside the house, the killer with a hook for a hand, and the vanishing hitchhiker. We've heard of ghosts and ghouls and seen elaborate Hollywood depictions of zombies—they fill us with the kind of fear that dries up the next morning.

Lasting fear is another entity. There are other things that frighten us every time we find ourselves uneasy in the dark. Everyone's imagination goes somewhere when they see a shadow that might be out of place: a childhood memory or something they heard in passing from a friend. The kind of horror that sticks with us are the things we know are real, what we worry may befall us in a dark room in the seconds before we turn on the light.

There's a reason the great tradition of a campfire is to tell scary stories around it. We need a way not only to entertain us but to pass on the stories that mean something, the ones that hint at an unsettling thought: not everything in this world is as it seems.

This book is a collection of short scary stories told from the perspective of the person who experienced them. These are real people's accounts of the creepy, the occult—of their near-misses with madmen and paranormal entities. Each chapter is a short, stand alone campfire tale, a retelling of a frightening or gruesome incident that has stuck with the teller, they are all the more terrifying because they are real. Read with caution.

1

Peeping Tom

In high school, I was obsessed with movies and wanted to be a director when I grew up. My parents saved up and bought me a camcorder and I spent money from my after-school job at a restaurant buying tapes and editing equipment to play around with. A few months after my next door neighbor died his wife had a huge garage sale, and though my neighbor had never told me he shared my interest in making home movies, I found a bunch of blank camcorder tapes at the sale and his wife ended up giving them to me for free.

I went home and put the tape in and watched in horror as I realized how upsetting the contents were. Tape after tape I found footage of my home and the area around my home taken from outside the windows as my family and I remained oblivious. My bedroom seemed to be his favorite to lurk outside and you could often see the inside clearly if I left the blinds open. He would just stand there and breathe and record whatever was happening inside.

It was chilling enough until I saw footage of a cabin about

3

an hour and a half from my home where I'd gone with some friends the previous summer. He had been outside the cabin filming and had even gone inside to film our beds and go through our stuff while we had gone into town for groceries.

It seems strange that his wife wouldn't have checked the tapes to see what was on them given that her husband had just passed away and she could be getting rid of irreplaceable family memories, but then again, maybe she had an intuition about what she would find and the kind of person her late husband really was.

2

The Man Outside

I always check the blinds before I go outside. For years people have made fun of me when they witness this and my husband thinks I'm crazy. We live out in the country and we've never had an issue with someone trespassing, but I still lean over every time I'm going out the front door and make sure no one's out there first.

One night I was about to go to bed when I realized I left my phone charger in my car. I had put it in my purse that morning because the one I had at work broke and only just remembered it as I left, placing it on my passenger seat. I needed to charge my phone and I didn't have a reason to be afraid of the ten yards from my front door to my car parked in the driveway, but I peeked out the window anyway.

I was running on such instinct that my hand was already on the lock, about to flip it and open the door when my brain registered that what I'd seen wasn't normal. I shifted my weight back and looked again, squinting to see in the dim light by the garage we leave on all the time.

I saw a man crouched by the front door holding a hammer. He wouldn't be visible from the little window on the front door. You wouldn't even see him until he was right next to you. I screamed for my husband and watched him book it down the drive. I didn't see him get into a car but he must have gone somewhere. We called the cops and they couldn't find any sign of him.

We invested in some flood lights night next day, and no one made fun of my habit again.

Message on the Mirror

I was babysitting for a new family in town one night. After the couple left, the kids were playing in the living room and I went upstairs to use the bathroom. I turned the light on and saw a message scrawled across the mirror in red lipstick: *tonight is the night evil begins.* I freaked out and made the kids go in their bedroom so I could lock the door. I called my mom and she came over and stayed with me until the couple returned. They seemed bewildered by the message on the mirror and claimed they had no idea how it got there. They were persistent in trying to hire me for the next few months but I never babysat for them again. I heard something similar happened to the next babysitter they managed to hire.

The "Body" in the Road

I've heard of things like this happening, but I thought it was an urban legend.

In college, I used to go home on the weekends to do laundry and eat free food and hang out with my family and high school friends. I was a night owl so I'd stay as long as possible and then drive the three hours back to school in the middle of the night. This is in Nebraska so even when it isn't the dead of night it's easy to find yourself totally alone on the road.

One Sunday night I was driving back to school and it was around 4 AM. I wasn't too far out of my (small) town toward the city yet and as usual, the roads were completely deserted. Up ahead, I saw what looked like an accident. There was a car pulled halfway off the road onto the shoulder and I saw a body in the middle of the road.

Needless to say, I was extremely creeped out—but I also had these feelings of wanting to stop and help if someone was hurt and needed medical attention. Eventually, my rational side won out and I decided to drive around the accident and then call 911 after I made it around and was on my way. I'm a small guy and something about the situation didn't seem right to me, or perhaps I was just too scared to stop and get out of my car in the dark to investigate.

I drove on the shoulder on the opposite side of the road, clear from the other car and the "body" on the road. When I was about ten yards past the accident I looked in my rearview mirror, ready to pick up my phone and call the police when I saw a handful of people coming up from the ditch where they'd been hiding behind the car on the shoulder. The "body" in the road was now standing up, watching me drive away.

He Could See Me

I was trying to make friends in my new city so I went to a party a coworker invited me to. I ended up having too much to drink because I was trying to calm my nerves and have fun with strangers. Uber wasn't a thing yet so I decided I'd just sleep it off in my car and drive home in the morning.

I woke up in the dead of the night and the city street was so eerie. It had been well populated around bar close when I passed out but now it was deserted. I could just see by the light of some street lights and the glow of the moon. I wondered for a minute what had woken me up before I heard a scratching noise on the passenger side rear window.

I'll never forget the look on the guy's face who was crouched outside my car, staring at me and trying to get my attention. When he saw me he grinned and pressed his open mouth against the glass and then made a chomping motion with his teeth barred and giggled wildly.

The worst part was there was nothing I could do. I knew I didn't want to risk driving drunk but I didn't want to get out of the car and run away either. In the end, I took my jacket off and put it over my face and just tried to go back to sleep knowing he was still out there. I heard him walking around the car tapping at the glass for what felt like hours as I hid in plain sight and prayed for him to go away.

The Night We Didn't Come Home

A few years ago I had a shitty job where I was forced to work third shift (nights) while my wife was working a normal day job. On the day my sister-in-law went into labor, my wife drove to the hospital after she was done with work and spent the night there. I arrived home early the next morning and entered the house to find the electricity wasn't working. After searching the house I realized someone had broken in through a basement window and cut power to the house through the circuit breaker down there. Nothing was taken from the home and the window in question was not visible from the front of the house. Slowly it dawned on me that someone had been watching us. They knew there was a window of time between when I left for work for the night and when my wife returned home—and that she'd be there alone for hours.

The Man at the Door

I grew up in a small suburb about an hour from a mid-sized city. I always felt totally safe everywhere. It was just a normal, idyllic place and I lived in a newish neighborhood with my family in a split level house. Our dining room was upstairs, but because of the open design, you could still see the floor below it as well as the foyer and front door. One night while we were eating dinner a man came to to the door and I went to answer it. He said he was lost and needed directions and kept looking between me and the rest of my family he could see upstairs.

I can't describe the terror I felt fill my body when I was talking to him; I've never experienced fear like this. His request was weird (it wasn't the kind of neighborhood you'd get lost or need directions in) but nothing about him should have been so unsettling. I gave him directions and he left. I deadbolted the door and ran up the stairs and felt afraid for the rest of the night. It was just a feeling I got. A feeling that if my family hadn't been at home and visible from the front door that I wouldn't be here today. I've never gotten a vibe like that from someone before that or since then (and it's been ten years). I'm still waiting for the day his face shows up on the news as a kidnapper or something.

8

The People in the Field

I'm a big guy so not a lot scares me. I used to be in the habit of walking in the middle of the night when I had insomnia. I hated lying in bed waiting to fall asleep, so instead of tossing and turning I'd get up and walk around my neighborhood for an hour and then I'd fall back into bed, dead tired, and sleep.

One night I'd taken an even longer walk than usual, convinced that returning home anything less than completely exhausted would be a waste. I found myself on the deserted grounds of the town's high school soccer fields—the school on one side and woods on the other. I decided to cut through the field to the street that would eventually take me home.

About halfway through the field, I saw something in the near darkness towards the very edge of the woods. Half a dozen shadows emerged from the forest and started walking toward me, slowly but steadily. I shouted out a "hello!?" to them but no one responded; they just kept walking towards me.

I turned around and saw that behind me, a similar group of people (?) had come from the woods and started to spread out in a kind of semi-circle around me. I turned around again and booked it toward the school. I'm lucky I was in shape from all those nighttime walks. I have no idea who those people were or what they would have done if I hadn't been able to get away.

That was the last night I took an insomnia walk.

9

The Watcher

When I was in high school, I used to babysit for this family a few blocks over. The dad ran a business out of the home, so one of my duties while I was babysitting was to make sure I answered the phone so I could take a message in case it was one of his clients calling. After a few months, I started getting creepy calls.

The man on the line would say awful things to me. He talked in a whisper and would describe what I was wearing. He said he was my "watcher" and that he was always watching me even though I only got the calls when I was babysitting. I eventually stopped complaining about the calls to the family because I could tell it annoyed them and I couldn't lose the babysitting job. Besides, the dad always gave me a ride the three blocks back to my home so it wasn't like I had to be out alone after getting the calls.

At the end of the school year, I moved a town over to live with an aunt and started attending a community college that summer. Because of the move, I never babysat for the family again. I forgot about the calls until a few years later when I saw the dad of the kids I was babysitting in the paper. He'd been accused of stalking and sexually assaulting a teenage girl who worked for his family. I don't have any proof, but seeing the way he smiled in that photo clicked things into place for me. I believe he was the "watcher" calling me all those times and I think something bad would have happened if I kept babysitting for that family.

10

Selfies from Hell

My older sister has a story about camping by herself in the '90s. She spent a summer as a backpacking guide in the Boundary Waters canoe area in northern Minnesota and decided to spend a week on a solo backpack before heading home in the fall. She said it was a perfectly normal trip, just like the ones she had been taking all summer in the same area.

She never had a bad feeling or anything—except, she had brought along a disposable camera to document the trip and have pictures to show family back home. There was a little dial at the top that showed how many pictures you had left before you used all the film. She said that there were a few times she swore she was keeping track of the count correctly so she could get photos of all her favorite places along the way, but when she would look she had fewer shots left than she expected.

She finished the trip and packed her stuff up and came home. Eventually, she brought the disposable camera in to get the film developed. When she got the photos back there were the pictures she had taken of the lakes and woods, along with photos taken of a nude man in a ski mask. They were crude "selfies" before selfies were a thing and they were interspersed throughout the rest of the photos she had taken, meaning the person in the photos had followed her on multiples days, seemingly for no reason other than to take creepy photos of himself with her camera.

What I Heard When I Pressed Pause

I was taking the bus home late at night. It's always empty and full of crazies but I got used to it. I usually just sat down and put my headphones on and listened to music until I got home. One night, a man sat next to me which I thought was strange since there were many open seats where he could sit by himself, but again, the bus at that time was usually full of strange people. I ignored him and focused my attention out the window.

Eventually, I became aware that this man was mumbling something to himself. I discreetly paused my music and tried to make out what he was saying. It turns out I'd been sitting there quietly for a good fifteen minutes while this man sat next to me talking to himself about how he should "stab this woman" and "show her what he can do."

I was terrified, but I felt like I couldn't move or alert him in any way. I didn't know if he would get angry or aggressive if I tried to get up so I was forced to sit there quietly listening to him until ten minutes later when he finally got up and got off the bus.

She Didn't Tell Me Someone Died There

One summer during college I took a job as a counselor at a Girl Scout camp. I was in charge of a cabin full of girls that would change from week to week as new campers came in, but I stayed in the same cabin all summer.

As time went on, I noticed weird stuff happening. Girls complained of nightmares which I thought was normal—except that all the girls seemed to be having the *same* nightmares. They all talked of a mean old man who had a scar on his face and chased them through the camp up to the cabin where they locked themselves inside while he banged on the doors and windows.

There were other strange things, too. Returning to the cabin to discover the lights on while we'd all made sure it was off before we left as a group for dinner or an evening activity. Meals were mandatory and activities were camp-wide—no one should have been off on their own to turn the lights on once we'd left the cabin for the evening. I also noticed that any food or water bottles I had in the cabin tended to disappear. At first, I blamed the girls because they weren't allowed to have food of their own so I thought maybe they were looking through my bags to steal the candy bars I'd stored there for a little pick-me-up. But again, like with the lights, there just wasn't any reasonable time in which anyone would be alone long enough in the cabin for them to go through my bag unnoticed.

At the end of the summer, the girls had gone home and the staff spent a tiring weekend packing the camp up and cleaning everything from top to bottom. On our last night, we were having a big bonfire and socializing and generally having a great time saying goodbye to each other. As I was getting ready to return to my cabin for one last night of sleep the camp director came up to me and asked in a kind of strange way how the summer had been. I told her the campers were exhausting at times but that I really enjoyed the work and I hoped to be back next summer. She pried a bit more and eventually I realized she was asking if I'd noticed anything strange about the cabin. It turns out that while the camp was closed up for the winter a homeless man had broken into this particular cabin and evidently spent a few weeks there before the owner of the camp discovered his body there at the beginning of spring.

The camp director even came with me back to the cabin where she pulled one of the bunk beds away from the wall and showed me a number of lines that had been carved into the wall—tallies they thought meant he was tracking each day that passed. I did go back to that job the following summer but on the condition I was assigned a different cabin.

The People in my House

As I was pulling my car into the driveway late one night my headlights illuminated two people in my living room. I owned my home and lived alone.

I immediately put the car in reverse and called the cops. I waited for them to get in the driveway before I returned. I sat out there while they searched the whole house and they couldn't find any trace of anyone breaking in or even being in my house. When I went inside I saw nothing was out of place. I convinced myself that it had been a long week at work and my mind was playing tricks on me— maybe it was a weird reflection from my lights in the window. That is until I talked to a neighbor a few days later and he told me he saw a couple going into my house the evening in question. He thought I knew them because they seemed to have a key.

I Was His "Friend"

In high school, there was a home on my block that was constantly between occupants. For whatever reason, it just changed hands a lot. We joked that perhaps the house was haunted, but my high school self wasn't worried about that at all. I used to sneak in through an unlocked basement window and hang out there alone and veg out when I needed space. Frequently I'd be there alone for a few hours listening to music on my headphones.

One Saturday afternoon I was hanging at the empty house listening to music and staring off into space. I was laying on my back and didn't notice anything weird happening. That's the afternoon I realized I wasn't the only one who liked to hang out at that empty house.

When I packed up my stuff a few hours later and went down into the basement to leave via the window I passed by the door to the room I'd been hanging out in. Someone had etched into the back of the door a crude drawing. It wasn't well done, but even with my adrenaline going I could tell it was supposed to be a sketch of me laying on the floor, my headphones wrapped around my head.

Underneath it, scratched into the door, was the word 'friend.'

A Bad Feeling

In 2002 I moved to Los Angeles was living in my first apartment alone. I didn't have a lot of money and my neighborhood wasn't that great, but it seemed safe enough and I was excited to live in a place alone so figured I could handle myself. One morning I got ready for work, grabbed my bag, and went to head out the door but the door wouldn't open.

At first, I thought I'd forgotten the lock was turned so I double checked it a few times but the door was totally stuck. I freaked out, suddenly claustrophobic in the small space and annoyed that I was going to be late for work. I picked up the phone to call my landlord when I heard gunshots outside. I ran to the door and it pulled open smoothly. I thought better of it and shut and locked it again, waiting for the police to come before I opened it again.

Later that day I found out there had been a shooting directly in front of my building, at exactly the time I would have been walking out the door. I wasn't the intended target, obviously, but I think someone was watching out for me, making sure I wouldn't get caught up in someone else's violence.

16

Premonition

A few years ago I sold my car to the uncle of one of my friends who was a mechanic and frequently bought cars to fix them up again before reselling. I bought a different car from someone else and drove it home and parked it in my driveway. The next morning I woke up from the most realistic nightmare of my life. In the dream, my husband and I had gotten into my car to drive to work like normal (he drops me off on his way so we only have to use one vehicle) and we gotten in a gruesome car accident that left us both thrown from the car and horribly mangled on the side of the road.

I've had bad nightmares before but nothing remotely like this. I felt like it was a premonition and pleaded with my husband until he agreed to take the day off with me. I've never done anything so dramatic before, but I was that convinced that something was wrong with my new car and we'd be terribly injured if we drove in it again. Even just sitting at home I felt so much anxiety I was nauseous for the whole morning.

My husband got the idea for me to call my friend's uncle to

whom I'd just sold my previous car to see if he'd do us a favor and come check it out and confirm that it was safe to drive. I called my friend to see if her uncle was around; she sounded upset like she hadn't expected it to be me who called. Instead of asking for her uncle, I asked him why she seemed upset. I came to learn that her uncle had just been in a really bad car accident in my old car where he had been thrown from the vehicle and injured horribly.

Screams in the Dark

I used to live in a very beautiful but very rural community in Appalachia. I grew up there and it felt safe to me, so going on night hikes with my girlfriend was a normal thing. I had a gun back in my truck, but I didn't bring it with me because my only concern was bears, and they weren't around that area. We'd gone on this hike many nights before when the sky was clear and it wasn't that dark out, but for some reason, we both felt uneasy on this night. I just kept hearing a little voice in my head saying "turn back."

When we were about three-quarters of the way to our usual summit I couldn't take it anymore and I told her I thought we should turn around. Later she would tell me she'd been feeling apprehensive all night too; she was as eager as I was to get the hell out of there. No sooner had we turned when we heard a bloodcurdling scream in the middle of the dark. A second scream broke out in another location, then a third, then a fourth, then a fifth.

All around us, we could hear people hidden in the woods only a few feet away from us screaming at the top of their lungs in the dark. We ran out of there as fast as we could, totally full of adrenaline. I scoured the local paper that entire summer looking for anything that would make sense of what we'd experienced, but no one reported anything weird happening in those woods that summer.

18

Last Text

The day my mother passed unexpectedly I woke up to a text from her that said: "I love you, too."

It wouldn't be abnormal for me to have texted her "I love you" and she responded with "I love you, too," but I hadn't talked to her at all the previous day. I had no memory of texting her recently that I loved her and my message history confirmed I hadn't sent a text like that. My sister called and told me of her passing before I was able to respond to her, but I like to think that a phantom text from me to her did exist and that she died shortly after being comforted by a reminder of my love for her.

The Man in the Window

I used to have a weekly overnight babysitting job for a couple who frequently spent nights in another nearby city caring for one of their ailing parents. It was an easy gig because they only had one kid who was eight years old and pretty independent. I just played with him for a few hours and got him ready for bed and then got paid for another fourteen hours while I watched TV, raided their fridge, and slept.

The one thing I *hated* about the job, however, was the house. It was a somewhat modern house in the country and they had big open windows and the style was such that there weren't any curtains I could close. I just had to watch TV and live with the anxiety of knowing someone outside could be watching me and I'd have no idea.

One night I was sitting down in the living room and I thought I heard a noise so I turned the volume on the TV down. Sure enough, what I heard was a slight *tap, tap, tap*. I looked around and didn't see anything out of place so I assumed it was a noise from a tree or something outside. But every time I turned the volume back up I heard that same *tap, tap, tap*. Finally, I turned the TV off altogether and started walking around the house. As my eyes adjusted to the darker room I saw a man outside the window, fingernail pressed to the glass, making that *tap, tap, tap* noise and smiling at me.

I freaked out and sprinted upstairs to check on the kid, but the worst part was that there wasn't a phone upstairs so I eventually had to creep back downstairs to grab a phone and call the police. I tried to avoid looking at the window but I snuck a glance and he was still there, just watching me calmly.

I locked myself the kid into his bedroom and waited for the police. They never found any trace of someone around the house and I suspect they thought I was some kid playing a prank but I know the person I saw was a full-grown man and that he just stood there enjoying the fear he caused me to feel.

20

Unexpected Company

I went to my mom's house in the middle of the day to pick up a sweater I'd left there a few days earlier. She was at work, but I often popped in to pick up something or leave her some vegetables from my garden for her while she was at work. When I walked in the door there was an elderly man seated at her breakfast table. He looked up and smiled at me and I assumed my mother was home from work that day and entertaining a neighbor for breakfast. I smiled politely and said hello and explained I was just grabbing a sweater. I then walked out the door and sent a text to my mom on my way to work saying I'm sorry to have missed her and interrupted her breakfast company. She called me back freaking out because she was at work and had no idea who was in her house.

Scratches

I heard a story at a slumber party I was at in high school about an old lady who snuck into your bed and scratched your face or back if you said you didn't want to have kids. It was a totally cheesy urban legend type thing, but something about being in someone else's house and hearing this story really creeped me out. Well, the other girls could tell that it scared me and gave me crap about it. Eventually, they made me say out loud that I never wanted kids, ever, and this lady couldn't do anything about it. We laughed about it and I actually wasn't scared when I went to sleep that night because I was surrounded by other girls. I woke up and everything was fine and normal. The next night, however, I woke up in my own bed with four scratches down my back as if they'd come from a single hand.

The Message in the Closet

In 8th grade, my family moved into a house where another family had lived before. I found out from the kids in the neighborhood that they moved away after the family's 4-year-old daughter was killed in the home in a freak accident. The mother was leaving for work and accidentally ran the kid over in the driveway. Everyone felt really bad for them and understood why they moved away right after with their other daughter who was 13 or so at the time.

I never told anyone, but some nights I swear I could hear a little girl crying somewhere in the house. At first, it was so real that I wandered around the house convinced that somehow a kid had gotten lost and needed help, but I never found any real person making the noises. This went on for years and I just got used to it.

Five years later I was leaving for college and my mom was going to turn my room into a nice guest bedroom where I'd stay when I came home, but she could also use it as an office most of the time. One of my jobs was to strip the entire room of the wallpaper that had been there since before we moved in. I got to a section in the closet and noticed it was patched in with glue as if it had been stripped away and then hastily replaced. I scratched around the corners until a small section of wallpaper easily came off. Underneath in black ink, someone had written "It wasn't an accident. They're going to hurt me, too."

23

My Dad's Laugh

My dad passed away nine years ago after he'd been sick for a long time. The last week my sister, brother, and I were all staying at my parents' house, spending some time with Dad and helping our mom care for him. He had always been so gregarious that the house felt extra quiet with him being sick, even with all of us there.

One night we were all up late (none of us were sleeping well) and ended up playing a game of cards around the kitchen table while Dad slept in his bed upstairs. We're a competitive bunch and even though it was late and we were all emotionally drained, the game gradually got livelier and livelier. Against all odds, there was even a moment where I was enjoying myself so much I started doing the kind of deep belly laugh we used to do when we were all playing games growing up, the kind where I wanted to stop because I could barely breathe, but I just couldn't. The laugh was contagious and soon we were all in a fit of laughter.

In the midst of this, I heard, very distinctly, my father's loud, booming laugh. I looked up and it seemed like everyone else had heard it too. Everyone seemed frozen in place, being so familiar with something we haven't heard in months. My mom went to check on Dad and he was sound asleep. He passed later that week. We've talked about how we all heard that same laugh and how somehow, it meant that our dad was with us, enjoying his family one last time.

24

They Weren't Really Ghosts

I've been into ghosts my entire life. I started seeing them when I was ten, and for the next ten years, I read everything on the paranormal I could get my hands on. I got involved with the paranormal society in my town, made a lot of friends, and went on some investigations. I truly felt lucky that I had found my place in the world.

Unfortunately, when I was 21 I was diagnosed with a debilitating health condition which sometimes causes hallucinations. I learned that the "ghosts" I thought I was so good at seeing didn't mean I was a gifted paranormal investigator, just that I had an illness which messed with my mind sometimes.

25

I Almost Found the Bodies

In high school, I was at a party thrown by a kid I didn't know very well. I always got a bad vibe from him but he was friends with a lot of my friends and they all wanted to go. Everything was cool and I was actually enjoying myself sitting out by a fire and talking with everyone until I got cold. I asked everyone if they wanted another drink and then went inside to grab some beers and hunt around for a blanket I could take out to the fire. I was just about to open up the hall closet when the host came in and started screaming at me about how I was invading his space and being a rude guest.

I've never seen anyone flip out like that so I just grabbed my stuff and headed home. A few days later it came out that he had murdered his parents and left the bodies in a closet in their house. He had invited us over to party with his dead parents in the house. It's sick enough on its own, but sometimes I think about what would have happened to me if I had found the closet where his parents were hidden and I was separated from my friends who probably wouldn't immediately notice my absence...

26

The Edge of the Cornfield

I grew up on a farm with my family and it generally felt pretty safe, but occasionally my mom would send me on chores after dinner when it was already dark. Wandering around near the edge of the cornfield really creeped me out, even though I knew my parents were right in the house. Chalk it up to having seen *Children of the Corn* and having an active imagination.

I was out there spreading compost for the chickens when coming from just a few feet away in the cornfield I heard a man's whistle. I sprinted back into the house where my dad was in there reading the paper and I told him what I heard. He headed out with a mag light but didn't see anyone. The next morning, however, there were cigarette butts on the ground near the entrance to the field.

He Wasn't the Mailman

When I was eleven I was home sick from school one day. My mom was a single mother and couldn't really afford extra time off so I convinced her I'd be fine and could just watch cartoons and make myself a sandwich for lunch. I was laying on the couch watching TV in the early afternoon when I heard a knock at the door. I wasn't supposed to answer it but the way the house was set up, you could see me laying on the couch from the front yard through a big picture window. I didn't want to be rude so I walked up to the window and looked out.

I couldn't see anyone but I heard a man over by the front door say, "Mailman! Got a package for you!"

I was a kid, so the idea of getting a package was really exciting to me and I really wanted to open the door and get it, but I knew I wasn't supposed to and had a bad feeling about it. I decided to go upstairs and look at the front door from my bedroom window, which had a clear view of the area. I looked out and saw a man. He wasn't wearing a mailman uniform. He didn't have a package. I looked out into the street and couldn't see a mail truck, either. I stayed locked in my bedroom until my mom came home and went back to school the next day even though I was still sick.

28

The Man in the Black Turtleneck

My best friend had a party and a lot of people ended up bringing their own friends so there were quite a few people there that we didn't know at all. Everyone was getting along and it was a really fun party until this guy in a black turtleneck showed up. I remember the black turtleneck because this was the middle of summer and it was hot, and this guy was wearing a throwback '80s turtleneck.

I never got introduced to him, but I saw him all night walking around or sulking in the corner and I just got the most intense bad vibes from him that I've ever gotten from someone in my life. I don't know how else to describe it but he just made my adrenaline flow. I had no idea who he was, but I was *scared* of him.

The next day we were all sitting around talking about the night before and someone brought up the guy in the black turtleneck. Everyone had the same reaction as I did but no one talked to him except my friend who was the host. She said he came up to her and started asking her if she had invited Jesus to live in her heart. My friend is not religious but is pretty polite and conflict avoidant so she just said no and then said she had to go help one of her guests.

The following day my friend found a handwritten note in her mailbox detailing what Hell is going to feel like for her. There were descriptions of the skin being pulled off her face and her limbs being cut off and tossed into piles for dogs to eat. We assumed the guy in the black turtleneck put it there but we didn't have any proof. All of us asked around to everyone we knew who had been at the party and a lot of people remember him and how creepy he was, but no one actually knew who he was or how he got invited.

29

The Blue Truck

One day my dad was late picking me up from school so I decided to walk home. It was a long walk which is why I didn't normally do it, but I figured he'd find me on the way and drive us home from there. After a little while, I noticed I'd seen the same blue truck going by me a bunch of times, and it was going slower than usual, too. This freaked me out a bit as my parents had recently had a big talk with me about safety and I was convinced pretty much all strangers wanted to kidnap me.

I ended up cutting across a neighbor's house and watching the truck go by before running home. I told my parents about it and they were proud of me for listening so well. In retrospect, I don't think they believed anything bad had been about to happen at the time, but it was a really big deal when a kid in my town was kidnapped a few weeks later. It was years before they found the body and a few more before they caught the guy who did it. He drove a blue truck.

30

He Didn't Answer the Door

When I was a kid, my mom wanted me to go to the elderly couple that lived next door and see if we could borrow a few eggs from them so she didn't have to go to the store. I knocked on the door and they didn't answer, but I could see the old man standing in the living room. I knocked louder and he didn't turn around. I thought maybe he just couldn't hear me, being old and all, so I turned the doorknob and it was unlocked. I walked in calling out for him. It was so strange to me that he wouldn't turn around until I got in the living room and saw that he wasn't standing at all. He had hung himself and I'd been trying to get the attention of a hanging corpse for the last ten minutes.

31

It Followed Me Home

I'm an avid hiker. One summer I had a goal to hike in every state park within a 100-mile drive of my home. It took me to some pretty off-the-beaten-path places and some trails that weren't often hiked on. On one particular hike, I stumbled across the body of a man who had obviously committed suicide. It was a horrible experience that I thought would end when I immediately returned and alerted the park rangers about what I saw.

But for months afterward I had vivid, lucid nightmares about this man where he would tell me horribly nasty things. The dreams were incredibly realistic and happened every single night. He wanted me to kill myself; he was trying to goad me into it. He told me I didn't deserve to live. He told me my wife and children were ashamed of me and would be relieved if I were to die.

It got to the point where I was really losing my mind. I couldn't sleep, couldn't focus at work, I was just physically and mentally exhausted. At that point, I would try anything so I went to a psychic who told me the spirit had attached itself to me and I needed to "cleanse" it. She sent me to a witch who burned some things in a bowl and made sure the smoke went all over my body. I didn't really believe in this stuff, but again, I was desperate. The night after that was the first night I got real sleep in months.

The man hasn't been back since, but I'm still uneasy. I can't believe that stuff like this really happens. I wouldn't believe it if it didn't happen to me.

32

"The Kind of Boy I'm Going to Murder"

I was on a late night bike ride around my quiet, suburban neighborhood one night when I couldn't sleep. After riding up a long, steep hill I stepped off for a moment to catch my breath and enjoy the night air. What I didn't notice right away is that I stopped about ten feet from a sleeping homeless-looking man who at first blended in with the shrubbery in the dark. He stirred and looked at me for a moment, I gave him a polite smile and started to get on my bike when he said: "you look like the kind of boy I'm going to murder." He said it matter of factly and then put his head back down and went to sleep. I got on my bike and pedaled pretty quickly out of there and back to my house. I don't go on late night bike rides anymore.

33

There's a Witch in the House

I had a dream once where I looked in the mirror and my reflection spoke to me calmly and said, "You need to wake up. There's a witch in the house."

I woke up and looked over at my wife who had blood all over her face. I shook her awake and turned on the light and asked her what happened. I thought she had a bloody nose or something but after we cleaned some of the blood off we found a cut on her forehead that ended up requiring stitches. We looked all over the bed for something that might have cut her but we never found anything sharp or out of place. Whatever caused it didn't even wake her up.

34

"Shh"

In high school, my parents went away weekends a lot because they were renovating my grandfather's old lake home into a cabin that the whole family could use. They'd usually leave on Friday afternoon and not return until Sunday afternoon. We lived in a smallish suburb so I guess word got around.

One weekend, my mom was sick so they decided to stay in town for the weekend, but because we parked our cars in the garage, anyone could probably assume they were gone like normal.

That Friday night I fell asleep watching TV in the living room. I was on a couch that was very clearly visible from a sliding glass door on our deck which had stairs down to our backyard. Basically, if you really wanted to, you could walk up and look directly into our house and see me since I was illuminated by the light of the TV.

I woke up suddenly and saw a man standing on the deck making the "shh" signal with his finger on his lips. I did not "shh." I screamed my lungs out and my dad came running down the hall to see what was going on. I pointed at the deck door and my dad saw the guy, too and sprinted toward the door, but in the time it took him to open the door and get outside, the guy had a lead and took off and my dad couldn't catch him. I don't know who he was or what he wanted, but I do know I was very nearly alone in that house where no one would have noticed something was amiss for several days.

35

Pictures of Me

A friend of mine worked at Walgreens in high school in the photo department. One day he cornered me at school and told me they had something "weird" to ask me. He asked if I was a part of an art project or something because at work he had recently developed an entire roll of photos of me that were taken in different locations and all of them seemed as if I was unaware that someone was photographing me. I obviously freaked out as I didn't know anything about these photos and I couldn't think of anyone who would do such a creepy thing.

I told my parents, and since I was a minor, the police ended up getting involved. Unfortunately, the name the person who dropped off the film used was "John Smith" and they never actually came and collected the developed photos, so there was no real way to figure out who had done this. I just had to move on and go about my life for the next few years knowing that someone could be watching me at any moment. There could be other rolls of film dedicated to me that this guy had taken somewhere else and I'd have no clue.

36

Blood Dreams

One night my friends and I were bored so we decided to play with her Ouija board. We were all joking around as neither of us believed in that kind of stuff but the board kept spelling out "you're all dead." I assumed some people in the room were colluding or something to scare us all. Their plan worked because I was pretty creeped out by the time I went home.

The next morning I woke up and looked at my hands, which were covered in blood. I ran to the bathroom and saw my face was also covered in blood. I started screaming until my mom came in the bathroom and asked me what was wrong. It confused me that she wasn't horrified at all the blood so I looked in the mirror and it was gone. I don't think I was dreaming it; I've never sleepwalked or had an experience like that before or since. I think whatever was talking to us through the board was making me see something that wasn't there.

37

A Cabin at Night

I was at a friend's cabin up north with a big group of girls one weekend. We went to a local bar and happened to meet a group of guys who were staying in a cabin on the same lake, about seven cabins down from where we were. That's quite a distance because each cabin is set up somewhat privately in its own bunch of woods, but it's not too far to walk if you're patient.

Late that night around the group at our cabin was settling down to go to bed and one of the other girls and I were wide awake. We decided to wander down to the guys' cabin to see if anyone was still partying.

The quickest path to their cabin was to walk through the shallow water along the lake's beach, hopping up occassionally on other peoples' docks, and pass the parts inhabited by cabins. All went well and we met up with the other group and ended up hanging out for a few more hours. The walk home got scary as we'd sobered up a bit by then and were aware of how dark everything towards the lakeshore was, how illuminated we were by the moonlight on the water, and how conspicuous we were, making noise even as we tried to wade quietly through the knee-length water.

We were about halfway home when we walked up on one particular beach to go around a dock. This cabin looked large and it was completely dark; we had no idea if anyone was inhabiting the place for the weekend or not. As we stepped onto their beach, we heard a series of loud bangs which sounded as if someone was banging their fist on a door. We froze, unsure if someone in the house had spotted us and were angry that we were trespassing—and the banging happened again louder this time.

We started to run through the water faster because we knew were making a lot of noise at this point and just wanted to get home. The whole time we were running home, we kept hearing that banging coming from the dark cabin. We got home and went inside and locked all the doors, hoping whoever was so angry hadn't followed us there.

Awhile later I learned that we may have been witnesses to a burglary or home invasion. One tactic people will use is to bang on the door for a while to make sure no one is home before entering. If they would have looked out toward the water, they would have found even easier prey than whoever may have been locked inside that home.

38

His Captive Audience

I sat next to a guy on a plane who calmly told me the story of how he killed his girlfriend and why he would never be caught. It was a three-hour flight and I couldn't alert the stewardess or even act like I thought his story was insane. The flight was full, and whatever happened, I was too close to him to risk him freaking out. Worse yet, no one else seemed to notice the topic of conversation because he was speaking in a low tone and as calmly as if he was discussing the weather.

After the plane descended and we were (finally) leaving, he turned to me and said, "Thanks for listening. That's the reason I love planes, always have a captive audience." It's so creepy to think that not only did he trap me into this terrifying conversation but it's something he does regularly, something he *enjoys*.

Scratches on the Window

I was housesitting for my parents while they were away and fell asleep on the couch in the living room. The couch is directly under a large picture window and you can't see the couch from the outside, but you'd have a clear view of the rest of the room, including the entryway by the front door and the staircase up to the bedrooms. I woke up in the middle of the night to someone tapping on the glass. I tried to convince myself that it was a bird or a branch or an animal, but the noise sounded deliberate and human.

I couldn't sit up and see what was making the noise because if it was a person, we'd be face to face and I was too chicken. So, I just sat there for hours, frozen in fear, listening to this tapping noise go on and on. I dozed off again after what felt like a few hours and woke up in the late morning. I felt relieved and assumed all of the fear was just my imagination going wild until I took a close look at the window. There were small scratches down the middle of the pane, about eye-level, that formed a group of tally marks. I had no idea what they were intended to mean, but they had definitely been done by a human, and they hadn't been there the day before.

40

The Nightmare that Saved my Life

My girlfriend and I were driving on a rural road late at night on the way home from a music festival. She had just remarked that the scene was like something out of a horror movie when there was a big *THUNK* and we ran over something. I thought it was probably a raccoon. A few miles later my low oil light popped on and I realized whatever we ran over had probably scratched a hole in the oil pan.

We pulled over and I called my brother and asked him to come get us and tow us home. It was the middle of the night and an hour or so away from him, but he's family so he said he'd be there as soon as he could.

My girlfriend and I sat in the car in the dark and had to roll the windows down because it was summer and we couldn't turn the car on to use the AC. It was creepy as hell sitting there in the pitch dark with the windows open; I just felt so vulnerable to anything that might be out there.

I dozed off and had a super vivid nightmare that there was a crowd of people around the car banging on every surface and telling us to leave. I woke up suddenly and checked the time on my phone; my brother would only 20 minutes away probably. Still, the dream scared me enough that I turned on my car and rolled the windows up. I didn't want to risk moving it, but I felt safer with them up and I stayed awake to keep guard.

Awhile later, my brother called me as I saw some headlights rolling up. He told me not to get out of the car because he just came upon a car that he thought was ours at first, a few minutes back. The driver and passenger doors were open and no one was inside but he saw some blood. We ended up running into his truck and just abandoning our car for the night instead of taking the time to hook it up in the dark.

On the way to his house, we called the cops and told them about the suspiciously abandoned car, as well as informing them that we'd left ours on the road for safety reasons and would be back for it the next day. We never got a call back about what happened to those people or why there were two cars forced to pull over in such a short space on a rural road, but I get a sick feeling in my stomach every time I think about whether we might have been a slightly more difficult target than the other car because I had the instinct to roll our windows up.

41

The Outgoing Call

When my wife and I first got married I worked nights which left her alone in our rented house in a crummy part of town. It wasn't ideal but it paid better than the other shifts and we were trying to save money to start our lives together. One night I was at work and on break when I got a call from my wife. It was one in the morning so I already knew something was wrong and she wouldn't speak on the phone, she was just sobbing uncontrollably. The call ended and subsequent calls to her phone weren't answered so I drove home frantically to see what was going on.

I parked in the driveway and ran upstairs, noticing on the way that the power was off in the house because none of the lights would turn on. When I got to the bedroom, I found my wife asleep in bed. I woke her up and she had no recollection of calling me and said she had gone to sleep like normal. We checked her phone and there was indeed an outgoing call to me, but her phone was plugged in on the dresser, out of her reach from bed.

After I calmed down and we laughed at how weird the situation was, I began to investigate why the power was off in the house. Finally, I went outside to discover that the power line had been cut. To me, that meant only one thing—someone was planning on breaking in and I had interrupted them in the process.

—

42

Hitchhiking

I know it's incredibly stupid, but I used to hitchhike home from the bar when I was younger. I didn't have a lot of money for taxis so I just trusted random people I'd meet on the street to drop me about ten blocks down the road from where the bars were so I wouldn't have to walk in heels. I tried to stick to young people who looked like me because I thought they would be the safest.

One night, I get in a car with a young couple who were pretty extroverted and asking me a bunch of questions about my life, what I did that night, etc. Everything was going well until I realized they drove past my block. I told them they passed my street and they could just stop at the next corner and I'd walk back. They didn't stop.

At this point, I started really freaking out but I made myself pretend to be calm and kept joking with them. They kept their happy front on and started talking about this party I should come to with them (as if I had a choice). I agreed and waited until we were at a stoplight and flipped the lock button up and hopped out of the car. I could hear them freaking out, but luckily there were some other cars around so they didn't do anything but peel out and drive away when the light turned green. I don't know where they were taking me or why they didn't drop me off, but the whole thing was a lot more sinister than our joking conversation let on. I learned a lesson that night and haven't hitchhiked since.

43

Missing Time

My girlfriend and I were taking a night walk around a lake in our town. There's a paved path and there are lights, so it's not deep in the woods or anything. We left the house at 9:45 PM and while we were walking we saw an owl in a tree. I remember we thought it was strange and we had a conversation about it and then continued the walk like normal.

We take this walk at least a few times a week. It's 3 miles from leaving our house to the path, around the lake, and back home. It usually takes less than an hour. When we got home I remember feeling a bit more tired than normal and looked at the clock to find out it was nearly 4 AM.

We started freaking out because there's no way we had just left home and walked for over 6 hours. We opened up her laptop, checked our phones, turned on the TV—but all the clocks said the same thing: it was indeed 4 AM. We sat up talking, trying to think of anything that could account for this missing time but every explanation we thought of seemed more implausible than the last one. Finally, we fell asleep and woke up in the afternoon feeling exhausted, drained, and sore. We both had flu-like symptoms that lasted the next few days.

I've done endless searches on the Internet trying to figure out if anyone has lost time in a similar way or in a similar place, and the only thing I've found is that a lot of people remember seeing owls right before an event like this.

44

He Probably Thought I Was Alone

My family has a cabin up north that's outside of a small town. It's on a lake where there aren't a lot of other properties and roads go from gravel to just dirt. No one goes on that last stretch unless you specifically know where my family's cabin is because there's nothing else in that area. Well, one weekend I had to work at my retail job until close on Friday but I really wanted to go up and enjoy the rest of the weekend with my family so I set out late, knowing I wouldn't get there until about 3 AM.

At the end of driving on the two-lane highway to this small town I noticed a large truck with KC lights had been following me for some time, but I didn't think much of it. I just figured that they were going to the same small town. However, when I passed the town and turned onto the gravel road, they continued following me which started to freak me out. I was alone, out of cell range, in the middle of nowhere, and if something happened, my family wouldn't notice I hadn't made it until morning.

As I started approaching the turn I'd have to make from the gravel road to the dirt one I started questioning what I should do. If this person was following me, turning onto the dirt road would show them where I lived, but continuing on the gravel road would just take us further out into nothingness.

Finally, I decided that going to the cabin was the best bet because at least there were other people there. As I approached, I started flashing my high beams and honking my horn. The lights in the cabin turned on and I saw my dad step out onto the front porch. I pulled up as far as I could and ran into the house. The truck sat there for a minute with the lights aimed directly at us before it reversed back down the road. My dad and I spent a sleepless night in the living room, watching and listening for any sign of someone coming back.

45

"I've Been Waiting for You"

I was installing one of those voice typing programs into my grandparents' computer so that they could send emails and use the Internet without having to type with their hands, which neither of them could do well. I had turned the microphone on to capture what I was saying and test the software out, but I was also messing around with my phone waiting for it to load when I noticed it had registered a voice command even though I hadn't said anything yet. I watched in horror as the words appeared on the screen, prompted by something I couldn't hear, "I've been waiting for you."

46

The Abduction That Could Have Been

When I was a little kid I was at a local park playing baseball with my older brother. We had to go home when the street-lights turned on but we were being slow that day and it had started to get dark already. As we collected our stuff and started to walk home I noticed a van had pulled up and the windows were down.

The path we were supposed to take home went right next to where the van had pulled up but I got a bad feeling from it. The guys inside were being rowdy and I heard them talking in Spanish about "getting one of those kids." Not a lot of people in this area speak Spanish but my brother and I were raised bilingual so we looked at each other and booked it into to the woods the other way. They weren't prepared to chase us on foot so we didn't really see them after that, but we sprinted all the way home. To this day I thank my mom for teaching us Spanish; I don't know what would have happened if we had gotten closer to that van.

47

Cabinets

Against my better judgment, I played on the Ouija board with a friend one night when he brought the board over to my house for "fun." Nothing too scary happened that night, though I had a really bad feeling the whole time we were playing it. The next afternoon I had my family over and it was a nice day so we were grilling outside and eating at a picnic table I have in the backyard.

After we all sit down I realize I forgot to bring out the salt and pepper shakers so I go back inside and freeze—every single one of the 20+ cabinets, cupboards, and drawers I have in my kitchen were wide open. Every person who was over was outside and accounted for, no one had been in the house since I brought out pitchers of water about ten minutes earlier. Luckily, nothing creepy has happened in my house since then, but I consider it a warning to never mess with a Ouija board again.

48

Sleeptalking

My ex-husband and I were nearing the end of our marriage and were fighting every day. The fights were pretty bad and I could tell we weren't headed to a great place, but I was in denial about needing to leave him. One night I woke up and he was sleepwalking, which he did occasionally. He was standing at the foot of our bed staring at me and I kept saying his name trying to get him wake up. Finally, he walked back over and got back in bed, but I could tell he was still asleep. As he got under the covers he put his head back on the pillow and said, "You're not going to be here anymore."

There was something about his unconscious words and actions that deeply unsettled me; it was more threatening than descriptive. I stayed up all night feeling creeped out by what had happened, and in the morning I took some of my stuff and moved in with my sister while we started the process of divorcing and moving on with our lives. Years later I heard the tragic news that he had killed his girlfriend one night. By following the case I found out that he told the police that he had been sleepwalking at the time, but he was eventually convicted anyway.

49

"I See You"

In college, I worked at our campus library and I'd often be the one to shut it down at midnight, where I'd have to go around and clear work tables of anything students had left behind and leave any books that needed to be put away stacked neatly on a cart for the morning workers. It was pretty creepy being in there alone at night, but in a way, I still felt pretty safe since the campus was enclosed and you had to go through a security checkpoint to get in after dusk.

One night I was there alone shutting everything down and I just had a creepy feeling that someone was watching me. I knew I was alone because before anyone is left alone, whoever else is working at night locks the doors and does a check to make sure no stragglers are still in the building, then the closer cleans up and locks the door again from the outside. Well, this night everywhere I went I kept looking around; I was sure that someone was in there following me around. Finally, I finished everything up and I went to clock out when I noticed one of the staff computers near the front door was lit up as if someone has used it recently.

I went over and looked at the monitor and saw a word document pulled up that followed through everything that I'd been doing since my coworker had left earlier that night. It read something like:

12:00 *alone. I see you.*

12:05 *group study rooms. I see you.*

12:07 *stacks. I see you.*

12:11 *media center. I see you.*

12:15 *reference tables. I see you.*

The scariest part was that I looked over at the door and it was still locked, meaning whoever had typed this was still in the library with me. I left my stuff where it was and left immediately, locking the door from the outside. By the time I got to another building and got campus security and went back to the library, the door was unlocked again and whoever was in there had left.

50

What the Cameras Caught

My first job out of college involved traveling a few times a year to different cities to check out venues my company would potentially host events at. It was intimidating to be in charge of something so big and to be traveling to strange cities by myself for the first time, but it was also very fun and exciting. On one trip I went to St. Louis and my researching skills were apparently not good because the hotel I looked up that I thought looked really nice ended up being in a bad part of town.

I didn't want to switch hotels because I'd have to explain to my employer what I did wrong, so I decided to just suck it up. Well, the last day I was supposed to be there I noticed a guy following me. At first, I thought it was my imagination, but I'd gone to four different places that day and seen him at every one. Finally, I went back to the hotel and noticed that he was sitting out front. At this point, I started freaking out and decided not to go back to my room. I went to the front desk and asked if there was a place I could speak to the manager privately. I was escorted to a back room where I told the manager what was going on and they called the police.

The manager was able to get surveillance footage of the day and you could actually see this guy watching me and later following me out the door. The manager went a few days back in the footage and saw this happen multiple times. We showed the police and the guy was brought in. I'm super lucky that this all went down the way it did because when they got a DNA sample they matched it to a string of sex crimes in the area.

51

My Grandmother's Necklace

My favorite grandmother left me a necklace when she passed away. It wasn't expensive jewelry, just a simple gold chain with a cross pendant that she had worn and reminded me of her. I wore it every day and loved having something from my family, so I was very careful with it. When I took it off, I made a rule to always put it back in my jewelry box so it wouldn't get lost.

One day, I couldn't find the necklace. I tore my entire apartment apart looking for it. I looked behind every dresser, in my pillowcases, underneath my mattress—every crevice I could think of. I was so sad but finally admitted it was probably lost forever.

A few years later I was going through a really hard time in life. I'd always struggled with depression and after I lost a job and a relationship, it was the worst it's ever been. There were a few days where I lay in bed and thought about just ending it all. One night, my thoughts wandered to my grandmother and I started speaking out loud to her and asked her to pray for me and help me get through this time, what she would have called a "dark night of the soul."

I got up from bed to take a shower and wash the tears away. When I came back into my room I got into bed, and as I moved the comforter I saw something fall to the floor—it was my grandmother's gold necklace. I have no idea how it was lost for so long, but I took its return as a sign from her that things were going to be okay eventually.

52

He Found Me in my Dreams

I was on a vacation when my family when I was a kid. We didn't have a lot of money so it was just a rinky dink family campground a state over with a cool pool/play area. My brothers and sisters and I would run around all day while our parents mostly vegged out at the campsite. On our last morning there, I woke up with scratches and bruises all over my body. I was kind of freaked out but my parents figured we'd just been careless while we had been on the playground and running around the woods the day before, even though I was the only one cut up.

I shrugged it off until my brothers and I decide we want to go for one last swim. We went to the pool and as we let ourselves in the little gated area I saw a big old man with long gray hair and a cross tattoo on his forehead. He was staring at me but I tried to ignore him until I made eye contact with him and he told me, "I found you in your dreams last night, boy." My brothers heard him and were creeped out too so we all decided to go back to our parents. The guy didn't make trouble and I never saw him again, but I still wonder if he was somehow responsible for the marks I'd accumulated the night before.

53

The Eyeball

Unfortunately, a severe form of mental illness runs in my family and I grew up visiting a few different relatives in psychiatric wards. I know it doesn't sound like a place for a kid (it always scared the shit out of me), but it's family and my dad would always lecture me about how lonely these people were and how they needed to be reminded of family and people who love them. One day I was tagging along behind my dad when a resident I didn't know shuffled up to me and held out their hand as if they had a gift for me. I thought maybe they were going to give me a piece of candy so I opened my hand up.

They dropped a human eyeball into it.

I found out later they had gouged it out of their roommate's face while they slept and no one had noticed yet. Dad never brought me to the psych ward again.

54

Robbie

I have a brother who is three years younger than me. When I was eleven he had an imaginary friend, "Robbie." The way his imaginary friend worked was that he was "real" and my brother did everything with him and talked about him as if he was any normal kid he was hanging out with. If you questioned him or referred to Robbie as imaginary, my brother would get red in the face and become very angry, saying that Robbie was real and that they were going to be friends forever.

I remember after a few months my parents suddenly got very strict about Robbie. They told my brother he wasn't allowed to play with Robbie anymore and that if Robbie came around he was to tell him to leave. This didn't go over well and it was a volatile few months while my brother was punished for mentioning Robbie and was very angry with my parents for taking his "friend" away, but eventually, the whole thing faded into the background.

It wasn't until I had kids of my own that I learned the truth about Robbie. I was joking with my parents about how my kids might get an imaginary best friend when they looked at each other with a weird facial expression. After a little prodding, I discovered the real reason they made Robbie go away was that they found out a little boy had previously died in the house. His name had been Robbie.

55

Speaking a Foreign Language Saved Our Lives

In college, I was in a study abroad program in East Asia. I went on a weekend trip to another city with friends I made in the program and we had the time of our lives exploring and practicing our language skills with the locals. We went clubbing one night and piled into a taxi late at night to go back to our hotel room. Being students and passionate about the area we were traveling in we knew the layout of the city, and it became clear the taxi was not taking us to the hotel but away from city limits.

My most assertive friend questioned the taxi driver in the local language about where we were going. He looked at us all in the rearview mirror for a good minute before he did a U-turn and took us back the way of the hotel. I don't know where he intended to take us, but I do know that speaking a foreign language probably saved our lives.

56

No One Did Anything

I was working on an international business degree and I hadn't started learning any foreign languages yet, but the perfect opportunity for me to do an overseas internship fell into my lap and I had to jump at it. It was incredibly frustrating to be dropped in a foreign country and have to make my way around without being super familiar with the local customs or knowing the language so my job afforded me a native counterpart who was working on his English and he served as a translator for me in a lot of situations.

Unfortunately, he couldn't be with me all the time, and one weekend I was feeling brave so I ventured off for a shopping trip by myself. As I began walking I noticed a group of men was following me. They started talking to me in a language I didn't understand (I don't think it was local) and it escalated to them screaming at me. I ducked inside a large department store thinking that they'd never be so brazen in public but it only got worse. The men continued to follow and harass me while the people around me *laughed* instead of telling them to go away. It was a total feeling of powerlessness as if the men could do anything and no one would stop them.

Eventually, as I sat there and sobbed the men left. I pretended to peruse items for over an hour just so I could be sure they were really gone before I left and hid in my apartment for the rest of the weekend.

57

It Wasn't Him

When I was in high school my older brother lived at home even though he had graduated. He worked the night shift at his job and would usually come home around 4 AM, make a snack, and then go to bed. Sometimes I'd wake up and hear him rattling around in the kitchen, and occasionally if I couldn't sleep, I'd join him and we'd have some nice late-night talks.

One night, in particular, I couldn't sleep and I heard the back door open and then someone shuffling around. I thought about getting out of bed to go down and hang out with my brother but I just had a really bad feeling about it. Something was telling me to stay in bed. Not thinking much of it, I went back to sleep.

In the morning, I heard yelling downstairs and woke up to find my parents arguing. It turns out, we'd been burgled because my dad had left the back door unlocked.

58

Mark

There was a big mall by where I grew up that was the "cool place" for the kids to hang out. When I was in middle school they instituted a rule that you had to be at least 17 to hang out there after dark, which only made it a more desirable place to hang out because you had to think of a way to sneak by the security guards that would question you if you looked school-aged. My friends and I made a routine of hanging out there on weekend nights by going in through the department stores and bypassing the guards at the normal mall doors.

One night we were hanging out in the food court sharing a basket of fries when a man approached us and introduced himself as "Mark." He told us that he knew of a new store in the mall where they were testing out a laser tag playground to see if older kids would be into it. Being middle school-aged kids, my friends and I were super interested in laser tag and were excited to help the guy out. He told us to meet him up on the fourth floor at the time the mall closed and he'd show us the setup.

At mall close, we went up to meet Mark where he told us but

got stopped on the way by a security guard. We told him we were special guests of a store and were going to test out a new laser tag game when he started looking at us funny. Eventually, he made us come with him to the security office where he called all of our parents.

I found out later that the mall was a hotbed for human trafficking and the "laser tag" story, in particular, was known to be used to lure kids into an area where they could be abducted.

59

Craigslist Roommate

I was looking for a new apartment and my budget was really small because I wasn't making a lot of money. I thought I could get a better deal by finding a roommate on Craigslist and splitting the rent. I found an ad that seemed ideal: a large private bedroom in a shared farmhouse outside of town with a young guy who was fixing it up to resell. I didn't mind a little construction chaos and I liked the idea of living in the country, so I contacted the guy and set up a time for me to look at what would be my bedroom.

I mentioned this to a guy friend of mine and he insisted on going with me, a decision I credit with (probably) saving my life.

When we got to the house I could tell the guy was annoyed I had brought my friend and mumbled something about how I "hadn't mentioned a boyfriend." He rushed through the showing and didn't really seem interested in selling me on the listing anymore. The weirdest part was that the small home didn't appear to have more than one bedroom although he'd told me there were two and that they were each large and private. He walked us to the front door and was trying to say goodbye when my friend inquired if the one door we hadn't opened yet lead to the second bedroom he was renting out. The guy started to say no but before he could protest my friend opened the door and revealed a small, dirty room with a mattress on the floor, a roll of duct tape on the dresser, and a camera set up on a tripod.

Luckily the guy let us leave with no problems (again, due to my male friend's presence). I called the police and let them know what was going on, but since a crime hadn't actually occurred they eventually told me there was nothing they could do.

60

The Late Shift

I used to work the late shift waitressing at a truck stop. I was young and friendly to everyone who came in until I realized the kind of trouble that could get me into. One older man, in particular, mistook my customer service friendliness for romantic interest. At first, I thought he was just lonely and enjoyed my company, coming in night after night. But his comments started to get creepy and I could tell he was asking questions trying to figure out where I lived.

One night I finished up work and went to the back room to discover my wallet was missing out of my purse. It was a scary 24 hours as I canceled my bank card and worried about how I was going to make rent with the few hundred dollars in cash I was now missing. The next night, the man came in and tipped me the exact amount of cash that was stolen. When I went to the back room at the end of the night I found my wallet on the table, all my cards were accounted for except my driver's license which had my current address on it.

He stopped coming in after that, but I feel like he was letting me know he knew where I lived and that he could visit any time he wanted.

61

Knocking

My boyfriend and I were staying with his parents for a month between when we had to vacate our apartment and when the house we purchased would be ready for us to move in. We were sleeping in his bed one night when we heard a loud knocking coming from his exterior wall. This bedroom was on the second floor but we still assumed his younger brother was messing around with us somehow. My boyfriend yelled, "Stop fucking with us," and suddenly the knocking came from all four walls at once, louder.

The knocking stopped after a minute and we were too afraid to get out of bed, so eventually, we just went to sleep. In the morning we questioned his brother and parents about if any of them had heard the knocking. They all (convincingly) seemed oblivious.

62

Writing on the Mirror

Whenever the subject of growing up or his hometown came up my boyfriend loved bragging that his childhood home was haunted. I thought it was funny but didn't put too much stock in his theory even as we arranged to spend a few nights there over Christmas.

I was alone in the bathroom taking a shower and I know I had double checked that the door was locked because I was paranoid about one of his family members walking in. The whole time I was bathing I just had this eerie feeling, like someone was watching me. I got out and was drying myself off when I looked up at the mirror and realized someone had written 'hi' in the steam.

63

"Check on your Daughter"

My mom used to feel like she was being watched in the house she rented when my brother was five and I was a toddler. We lived there alone as my dad wasn't in the picture and she bought drapes and curtains to cover up the windows but never shook that feeling the whole time we lived there. One day she was downstairs folding laundry while my brother watched cartoons and I was napping in my crib upstairs. The phone rang, my mom answered it, and all she heard was a voice that said: "check on your daughter."

Creeped out beyond belief, my mom ran upstairs to find that I had woken up and climbed out of my crib. I was crawling up my dresser trying to get a toy and the whole thing probably would have fallen on top of me and killed me if she hadn't caught me in time.

64

They Knew my Car

I used to have a CB radio to keep me company on long drives across the country as I traveled around selling college textbooks. One night I was on a particularly quiet stretch of road and hadn't heard anything for awhile when a voice came through talking about my car and license plate number and telling me he was going to rape me. I don't know where this person was as I hadn't seen another vehicle going my same direction in a while and I had no idea how they knew I had a CB. Nothing bad happened that day, but I got out of my job as soon as I could. I didn't feel safe traveling on my own anymore.

65

The Devil Couldn't Hurt Us

One night I stayed up late watching *Poltergeist* with my dad. My parents were really religious and afterward, I was really freaked out. Somehow my dad thought it would help to tell me that poltergeists aren't real but the devil is and what people think of as ghosts are usually actually demons. I was terrified and I kept asking him questions about ghosts and demons and how *hypothetically* you could get rid of one and whether they could hurt you. My dad told me to stop being silly and that because we were a Christian family, the devil couldn't hurt us and there was no reason to be scared.

We left the living room and walked into the kitchen to make a snack before bed. When we walked in every single cupboard and drawer was standing open. My mom was the only other person in the house and had long since gone to bed (and wouldn't have done something so strange anyway). My dad and I never discussed what happened but secretly, I always felt like it was a warning not to get too comfortable; whatever evil is out there in the world can get to you no matter who you are and what you believe.

66

Someone Was There

After graduation, I moved in with my uncle for the summer while I was looking for a job. He's a quiet dude and we mostly kept to ourselves, just enjoying each other's company occasionally and watching TV.

One evening I was sitting in my bedroom with the door closed. As I'd been sitting there playing on my laptop it had gradually become night, but I hadn't bothered to get up and turn a light on. I heard the front door open and someone walking around downstairs but I didn't think anything of it; I thought it was my uncle getting home from work. I heard the noises move from downstairs to the hallway outside my door and then to the bathroom next to my bedroom. I heard the distinct sounds of someone turning the shower on and the water running for a few minutes and then someone exiting the bathroom.

I thought it was weird of my uncle to shower in the middle of the evening, but not enough to get up and ask about it. Eventually, I went downstairs to get a drink and saw my uncle walking in the front door. I asked him if he just got home and he said yes. I asked him if he'd been in the house earlier that night and he said no. I was ready to dismiss my imagination as crazy before we went upstairs and saw that there were still droplets of water in the bathtub as if someone really had showered recently.

67

The Visitor

I had a big, old golden retriever, Barlowe, that I loved more than anything. In the past year, I'd noticed him aging even more, to the point where he wouldn't even get up to greet me when I walked in the door, so I got in the habit of settling down and decompressing a bit instead of immediately having to take him out for a walk.

One evening I got home from work and it was already dark because it was that time of winter when it gets dark in the late afternoon. I didn't turn the lights on because frankly it had been a long day and I just wanted to fall on the couch for a few minutes and relax before starting my night. As I lay in the quiet, I heard Barlowe shuffling around and saw his outline shuffling on the other side of the room. I called for him, but he just got really still and didn't come.

I shrugged it off and went into the kitchen to get a glass of water before going to my bedroom where I planned to change into some sweats and take Barlowe for a walk. When I flicked the light on, I saw Barlowe in a deep sleep on my bed. There was no way he would have gotten back in there and slept without me noticing. To this day, I don't know what was crawling around on all fours in my living room, but I know it wasn't Barlowe.

68

The Woman in the Kitchen

Growing up, I always had a bad feeling in my childhood home and I never liked to be alone there, ever. I didn't actually have any bad experiences, and so when I grew up, I assumed the "bad feeling" was just a kid thing. When I was 7 months pregnant last winter I went home to visit my family for Christmas. My husband had to work right up until Christmas Day so it was just my mom, my younger sister, and me for a few days.

One afternoon my mom told me she was running to the grocery store. Being 7 months pregnant I decided to just lay on the couch in the living room and soon I dozed off. When I woke up, it had gotten dark and since the kitchen light was on behind me, I could see a bit of the kitchen reflected in the window I faced as I lay on the couch.

There was a woman walking around and I assumed it was my sister, but I couldn't see clearly. I wasn't afraid at that moment, and I was about to open my mouth and tell my sister to come over because the baby was kicking, but I had an overwhelming feeling like I should be quiet and go back to sleep.

Awhile later I woke up again as my mom flicked on the lights and started putting groceries away. I saw my sister walking in the door with grocery bags in her hands and made a comment about her waking me up from my nap. They looked confused and my sister told me she'd decided to go with my mom to the grocery store.

69

The Body in the Lake

My cousin and I went swimming at the lake in our town like we'd done hundreds of times over the years. It was a sunny day and we were having a great time laughing and treading water and catching up. All of a sudden my cousin gets this weird look on her face and says she thinks a big fish swam into her leg because something slippery and solid brushed past her ankle. This freaked us out enough that we decided to go sit on the beach and tan for awhile.

About an hour later we were still at the beach when we heard some people talking loudly and some kids screaming. We got up and walked over to where a crowd of people had gathered on a rocky section of beach about 20 yards from the sandy part we'd been swimming in. A decaying human body had washed up there and gotten stuck behind a partially submerged log that jutted out from the shore.

We read in the newspaper later that it was the body of an older man who'd gone missing a week earlier, they think he went for a night swim by himself and drowned. To this day my cousin insists his body is what touched her leg in the water that day. She says it was "soft" and when she went to kick it away it seemed bigger and more solid than a fish, like nothing she'd ever felt in a lake before.

70

He Was Going to Take Her

I had to babysit my cousin one Saturday so I decided to take her to the mall. She was seven at the time and obsessed with this store that sells little girl clothes and accessories. She wanted to spend hours in there looking and touching everything. I was really bored so I was just kind of following her around and playing on my phone. At some point, I looked up and realized I had lost track of her.

I quickly walked around the entire store and finally found her at a display near the door talking to a middle-aged man who was crouched down and joking around with her. It seemed like he was telling her a funny story because she was smiling too. As I was watching he stood up and grabbed her hand and started walking with her out the door.

I walked up to them and asked my cousin if she knew who he was. I could tell instantly I'd interrupted something. The color drained out of this guy's face and his genuine smile turned into a really nervous, fake-looking one. He said, "I was just going to help this little girl find her mother," but I knew from his reaction he'd been up to something sinister and I'd caught him just in time.

I grabbed my cousin's hand and marched her away and reported the man to mall security, who (lamely) said they'd "keep a lookout." I had a long conversation with my cousin about strangers and made sure she understood she was never to go off with someone she didn't know, even if they said they knew her family.

71

He Didn't Know I Was There

I was in a public restroom in a mall and I'd picked an out-of-the-way one so I had some privacy to do my business. After a few minutes, I heard a guy walk in and go to the urinal. I could see just a little sliver of him through the crack in the stall. I heard the guy's phone ring and he finished up and answered. I could tell right away this wasn't a conversation he'd want someone to overhear, so I lifted my feet up so he could think (or at least pretend) he was alone.

I could hear the person on the other end of the phone screaming, but I couldn't make out what the words were, they just sounded hysterical. Then I heard this guy say, "Is she breathing?" and the person started talking at a normal volume because I could barely hear anything. At this point, I'm holding my breath because this is obviously a very serious situation and I don't want to involve myself in it, but I wasn't really afraid until I heard the guy talk again and he said, "Just make sure she doesn't leave before I get there." He hangs up, washes his hands, and leaves while I'm sitting there on the toilet with my mouth agape.

I want to think that my imagination was running away with me—that he wasn't on his way to go murder some girl—but I don't know why he wouldn't have told his friend to call an ambulance if someone had been in an accident where "Are they still breathing?" is a question you'd ask. He was stone cold about it too, like someone who was tired of cleaning up this kind of a mess.

72

Truck Stop Girls

I ran away from home when I was sixteen and spent a few months hitchhiking back and forth across the country. It was incredibly dangerous, but I was young, dumb, and it seemed better than the situation I left at home.

I mostly caught rides with truckers because that's who would take me. They wanted company (and sometimes they wanted more) but generally, they weren't a bad bunch, just wanted to listen to music and talk to me about stuff. A lot of them were even a bit protective, hooking me up with other guys they knew that were headed the direction I wanted to go in.

There were some bad guys, too, but there was only one really bad guy.

I'd had bad luck getting a ride out from this one particular truck stop. I'd been up all night waiting to find someone who would take me with them and finally, this guy overheard me asking someone else and said he'd give me a lift. I had a bad feeling immediately, but I felt like the decision was already made and I'd had bad feelings before which turned out to be okay rides.

We weren't even a few miles down the road when he started to seriously creep me out. He started lecturing me how unsafe it is for a young girl to be out on her own. He said things like, "These truck stop girls, they go missing and no one notices for months or years. It's almost like it doesn't count." I tried to be polite and thank him for his advice, but internally I was freaking out and wondering how soon I could ask him to let me out without making him angry.

Eventually, I made up a story and asked if I can get out because I'm having my womanly time and wanted to make an adjustment. I told him I could just hitch another ride after I had time to take care of my hygiene (I hoped this whole conversation put the possibility of raping me far out of his mind). He pulled over on the side of the road near a cornfield and I got ready to get out, but he controls the locks and my door is still locked.

He looked me in the eyes, reached over me, and manually unlocked the door and said: "run away, little girl." I scrambled down to the ground and ran as fast as I could ever remember running for a few minutes in sheer terror. I have no idea if he chased me or not, but when I came to my senses I just kind of sank to the ground in the middle of the cornfield and got into the fetal position and tried not to make any noise. I listened and didn't hear anyone coming, but I spent the better part of a night there, too scared to move.

73

Caught on Tape

I lived on a hobby farm outside of the suburbs. There were a lot of farm cats that weren't raised by me but wandered around the farm anyway. One day I noticed the body of one that had been eaten by an animal so I set up some game cameras to see if a coyote or something was wandering around.

The next time I found a dead cat, I went to watch footage from the game camera and hoped it would tell me what kind of predator I had on my hands. When I watched the footage, I saw a figure approach, turn the camera around so that it faced the fence it was sitting on (the screen went black, basically) and leave it there for a few minutes until the camera was pointed in its original direction and the dead cat was visible in the frame.

The only thing that would have moved the camera around like that is a human. I have no idea why a person would sneak onto my farm in the middle of the night to kill a cat, and I'm not sure I want to know.

74

Campground Horror

My girlfriend and I were at a normal pay campground in my area. It never felt spooky because we weren't out in the woods or anything. The campsites were fairly close together and there were typically at least a few other groups within shouting distance. This was in early October, so we thought we'd get in one more weekend away for the year before it got too cold.

When we arrived, we checked in and picked out our campsite. The worker told us there were a few families around but we were lucky because only one person had checked into the area by us. We drive to the site and get set up, get a fire going, and we're having a nice night enjoying a few beers and relaxing by the fire. Then we see our "neighbor" return to his campsite.

In the dark, we can see the outline of a big guy making a fire and tinkering around with his stuff. He's about twenty yards away, but we can hear him mumbling to himself. We don't think much of him until we go to bed a few hours later and we can still hear him talking to himself, only it's louder now.

He's talking about people disrespecting him and how "those

people don't know what's good for them." At this point, we get a little freaked out because we also notice that his voice is getting louder and he seems to be closer to our tent. We don't sleep, we just listen to him.

Eventually, we hear him spelling "R-U-N" over and over and we quietly decide that we need to leave. We had a whispered conversation and decide we are going to leave the tent and all our stuff and quietly walk in the dark to our car before unlocking it (which would make the lights turn on and alert him that we were entering our vehicle) and then quickly drive away.

This plan works and we drive an hour home and return in the morning to pack up our tent. I was relieved when I saw it was still there and the guy was nowhere in sight; I half expected him to have trashed our campsite. When we talked to the campground worker on our way out, I found out that after we left the guy had started wandering around the entire campground screaming about how he wanted to stab someone. The families felt terrorized and eventually the cops came and hauled the guy off.

75

Voicemails

I used to wake up with a voicemail on my phone every morning. I never heard a call come through and I never saw evidence of one on my call log, but this happened every night for a few months. The message was always the most horrific noises—static, screaming, gurgling noises, animalistic crying sounds—and then someone would say, "I'll see you soon." I had no idea what it could be or how it was getting onto my voicemail but I assumed it was some kids playing a joke on me or something.

It freaked me out enough that I decided to get a new phone number. The morning after, I woke up and checked my voicemail and felt a huge sense of relief when I saw that there were no messages. I went to work and checked the voicemail on my work phone like I always do and heard the same strange noises I'd been hearing on my phone. This time the voice said, "I'm always here."

76

He Wasn't a Cop

This story is still so terrifying to me that it feels like a dream or something that happened to someone else. I was home one summer alone while my parents were at work. I was twelve and it was the first summer I was allowed to not have a babysitter during the day.

A man came to the door and said he was with the police and he needed to check the house out for criminals. This scared me a lot as you can imagine, but I was under strict instructions not to let anyone into the house and this man wasn't wearing a police uniform. Also per my parent's instructions, I had opened the door to see who was there, but I left the screen door shut and locked so they didn't have access to the house.

I told the man at the door that I wasn't allowed to let anyone in but my mom was in the shower (this is what my parents told me to say instead of "no one else is home") and she could let him in in a few minutes. At this point, the man quickly reached up to pull the door open and I knew something was very wrong. Finding the screen door locked he took his keys out and began digging at the screen to get inside.

I started screaming and ran upstairs to my parents' bedroom where I locked their door, went inside the adjoined bathroom and locked that door as well and sat there and cried. A little while later I heard my mom's voice screaming at me through the door. Luckily, a neighbor had seen the man stabbing his keys at the door and called 911 and then my mom. The police were also there. I had to tell them what happened but they never caught him. My mom took a leave from her job and stayed home with me for the rest of that summer.

77

Under the Bed

I was kind of rough around the edges in my 20s and dated a guy who lived in a gigantic dilapidated house with six other guys. It was one of those big old homes in the bad part of town that used to be a mansion but was now drafty and run down. My boyfriend and his roommates did a lot of drugs there and no one cleaned basically ever.

I hated sleeping there with him because he had a really big old bedroom and I always felt like someone was watching us. Even with his arms wrapped around me, I just never felt safe.

After a few months of this, we had a big blow-up fight about how I couldn't see a future with him because of his drug use and lifestyle. To make up for some of the meaner things I'd said I offered to help him give his bedroom a good clean and hoped that it would be a little step towards a fresh start and a reduction in his bad habits.

I spent all day in there organizing and washing stuff, doing laundry, etc. while he passively helped. I had most things sorted out when I asked him to help me move his bed a bit so that I could clean everything that had gathered underneath it. I expected it to be dusty and full of stuff that happened to fall underneath there: empty water bottles, clothes, maybe a stray pillow. I wasn't prepared to find a human-sized nest dug out in such a way that it wasn't visible from the side. It was basically a mound of clothes with a hollow center filled with food wrappers.

We deduced that one of his drugged friends had been sleeping there some nights, pulling my boyfriend's clothes over himself to stay warm. I felt so grossed out knowing I'd slept in that room unaware of another person in it that I never went back to that house, which was probably a good thing because it led to that guy and me breaking up.

78

Thomas with the Top Hat

In elementary school, I suddenly had to start going to the doctor a lot and taking a lot of medicine. My parents told me I had bad headaches and the doctors and medicine were to fix them and make me feel better. I never thought that much about it until I was older and didn't live at home anymore. I was thinking about having kids and it dawned on me that I didn't really understand what my own childhood illness was.

The next time I was visiting my parents I asked them what kind of sickness I had. After some prodding, they finally told me that I was never sick. I had told them about my imaginary friend "Thomas" who wore a top hat and they freaked out because my dad's brother had had an imaginary friend "Thomas" with a top hat growing up who was always making him do bad things. My uncle used to torture neighborhood cats and bully kids, and he always said it was "Thomas" who made him do it. My uncle grew up to be a bad man and eventually ended up in jail.

My dad was being cautious and wanted to make sure psychiatrists didn't think whatever made my uncle so bad was genetic, but I guess "Thomas with a top hat" was just a coincidence.

79

Evening Run

I used to go for evening runs on the trail near my house. Not many people are around in the late evenings when it starts to get dark, but it's in a park in city limits, so it's not usually deserted.

One night I got going a little late and realized I was going to be doing the second half of the jog in the dark. I'm fine with this as I'm very familiar with the trail and feel safe in the area. There was enough light from light pollution in the sky for me to not be in the total dark anyway.

I was about three-quarters of the way home when I stopped to catch my breath. At this point, I noticed something smelled really bad around me, but I couldn't place what it was. I thought maybe there I was near a public garbage can and no one had emptied it in the last few days. Whatever it is, I don't like it and I decided I didn't need to catch my breath that badly so I continued my run home.

The next day after work I thought back to the smell and realized I didn't want to be stuck running in the dark again so I put my sweats on and hit the trail in the early evening. I got around three-quarters done again and I noticed there was a roped-off area up ahead and there was a police officer standing there.

The roped-off area was empty except for some dark stains in the grass but I stopped and asked the officer what was going on. He told me they found a body there in the morning. A woman had been killed a few days prior and the decaying body was transported and dumped along the trail. I filled him in on what I noticed the previous night and he confirmed that what I smelled was likely the corpse. Given that it had just gotten dark when I came through the scene, the officer told me I was lucky as I was probably pretty close to interrupting whoever was leaving the body there.

80

Cheap Hotel

My dad tells a story of when he was on a cross-country road trip in college. He and his buddy would drive until they couldn't keep their eyes open and sleep on the side of the road or get the cheapest motel room they could find. One night they were in a seedy roadside motel completely passed out from driving all day and the phone rang.

My dad answered and talked to someone from the front desk who said they're sorry to wake him but there had been some break-ins at the motel and he should check to make sure his door is locked and that nothing missing from his room. My dad hung up and noticed that the doorknob was actually moving as if someone was trying to jimmy it. He got up and ran to the door and started banging on it and screaming. Then, he looked out the window and saw a few guys running away.

The next morning as they're checking out my dad told the front desk clerk about the guys who tried to break in and thanked them for the warning. The clerk got confused and said he's never heard of any break-in attempts here before and that their protocol would have been to phone the police. He hadn't called my dad's room and he was sure no one else had, either.

81

My Grandfather's Visit

I lived with a few buddies in a house after college and we built a nice outdoor seating area and firepit. I was a smoker so I spent the most time out there just smoking and looking at the stars and being chill.

One night I was out there and started thinking about my grandfather who'd passed a few months ago. We were really close and I even started to tear up a little as I thought about how much I missed him and how I'd kill to have another one of our late night talks. As I was thinking about this, I saw a light in the house go on and saw one of my roommates walk into the kitchen and grab a glass of water. He looked out at me and I waved, thinking maybe he'd join me for a smoke, but he turned and walked back upstairs.

The next morning I asked him why he didn't come out and hang with me and he asked me if one of our neighbors wandered over. I didn't know what he was talking about so he explained that when he looked in the backyard he saw me sitting out there with an older man whose description fit my grandfather's.

82

Evil Little Boy

There was a little 7-year-old boy in my neighborhood that kind of freaked me out. He had pale skin and dark hair and black eyes so I thought maybe he just reminded me of the little boy from *The Omen*.

One day there was a family emergency and his mom frantically asked me if I could watch her kids while she and her husband went to deal with the situation. Of course, I agreed and went over there and told the kids we were going to have a surprise movie night. We watched a bunch of Pixar movies and it was actually pretty fun.

The other kids went to bed without a fuss but the creepy kid just kept following me around and saying he didn't want to sleep. Finally, I got him to go to bed by promising him I'd tell him a bedtime story. I asked him what kind of story he wanted to hear and he said: "one where my mommy dies."

83

The Man Who Takes Them Up to the Sky

I'm a mom of two kids. One afternoon I was cleaning up the kitchen while my three-year-old and six-year-old played in the next room. I noticed it had gotten a little quiet, so I walked towards the hallway to go check on them and overheard my three-year-old ask his older brother, "Do you think the man is going to take us up in the sky again tonight?" My oldest replied, "He said he'd be back tonight." No amount of questioning got either child to talk. We searched their rooms and made sure the windows were locked. My husband and I even slept on the pull-out in the living room so we could watch both of their doors. Nothing happened that night or any other, but that conversation still creeps me out.

84

The Lure

My friend lived a few blocks away from me in our city and we would walk home from each other's places late at night. It was a little risky just because in any city, it's never completely safe, but we had a system in place of texting each other when we got home, so we thought it was fine.

One night I was making this walk home when I heard a baby crying. Not just crying, but screaming in a way I've never heard from a baby before. I stopped and looked around and didn't see anything, but I started walking toward the noise just because it was so weird to hear a baby crying in a neighborhood where mostly 20-something kids lived. I realized the crying was coming from the middle of a parking lot behind the apartment complex next to mine. I couldn't see anything but I was hesitant to go investigate. I was worried because it really sounded like something was wrong.

My fear got the best of me and I speed-walked home where I called the police from the safety of my apartment. They sent someone to investigate and I left my number. I got a call from a police officer about thirty minutes later. He said he searched the area and didn't see or hear anything strange but he wanted to call me and let me know that men sometimes use recordings of hurt babies or children to lure women into an area where they can be abducted.

85

Headphones

A woman in my neighborhood was assaulted by her ex-boyfriend and almost died because I was playing a video game.

It was late on a Friday and I had my headphones on and was playing with the volume up. After a few hours, I decided to take a break to make myself a cocktail. Immediately when I took my headphones off I heard screaming and commotion coming from next door. It wasn't like my neighbor lady to be loud at all and she really sounded like she was in trouble so I called 911.

I found out later that the police had hauled away a guy with a Bowie knife. He'd already done a lot of damage by the time they got there, but she lived. Eventually, I talked to her about it and she was extremely grateful that I "saved her life." I just can't help but think about what would have happened if I had taken my headphones off earlier.

86

He Wanted to Keep Me Locked Up

I was bartending at a dive bar in my college town during the summer. Many of the students were gone and it was mostly townies who frequented the place. One night it was just a few patrons and me, and I was half an hour from closing the place down and locking up.

I asked an older man seated at the bar if I could get him something else because we were going to close soon. He grinned and looked at me and said, "Whenever I say what I really want, people to say I'm a dirty old man." I immediately got super creeped out but tried to laugh it off so the situation didn't escalate. I told him what we had on special and hoped he'd order a drink and leave me alone.

He said, "Do you want to know what I really want?" Again, I tried to steer the conversation to something non-creepy and I asked him what kind of drink I could get him. He ignored this and began telling me that what he really wanted was "a young girl like me he could keep locked up." To this day I'm still mad at myself for laughing politely as if he had made a joke, but I was really scared and I didn't want to make him angry. I pretended I had something to do in the back and called the police who did exactly jack shit besides escorting me to my car after close because "he's probably just an old drunk."

87

She Told Me Not to Call the Cops

I live in a nice suburb and never really worried about crime before this happened. I was woken up in the middle of the night by a frantic woman banging on the door. I could see out the window that she was dressed nicely and looked pretty normal for the neighborhood, but I still didn't want to open the door because I lived alone and it was the middle of the night.

I asked her what she wanted and she said she was running away from her husband who had beat her and to please let her in. I was still scared so I told her I was going to call 911 and she should just wait on the porch. I went to get my phone and when I came back she had vanished.

I called the police anyway and when they came they said they'd gotten another call in the neighborhood from another person who this woman had told not to call the police but to let her in, and the neighbor had gotten suspicious. They think this was a hoax used to gain entry to the house and there were likely other people waiting just outside my house to barge in if I had opened the door.

88

The Intercom

I'm almost 99 percent certain my apartment's intercom system saved my life.

I live in a neighborhood with a lot of gigantic old homes that have been turned into duplexes or small apartment buildings. The one I live in just looks like an old mansion on the outside but it's actually three modest apartments on the inside and there's an intercom at the front door so that I don't have to walk down from my 3rd-floor apartment just to let someone in.

Anyway, one night I hear someone knocking at the front door. I go to the balcony and look down and see a little kid looking up at me, he says he's lost and needs help. I told him I can call the police for him and he says no, he just needs to use my phone to call him mom to come get him. I say okay and go back inside.

I had planned to just go downstairs and bring the kid my phone, but something felt off about the situation to me. On a whim, I went over to the intercom and pressed the "listen" button and I heard the kid quietly talking to a gruff sounding man about how they were going to jump me when I opened the door.

89

Don't Ride with Strangers

In high school, I got into a fight with my friends and started to walk home from a party somewhat drunk in the middle of the night. It was a long walk (about 4 miles) but I was stubborn.

Eventually, it started raining and a car stopped and a dad-looking man asked if I wanted a ride. I accepted and got to thinking that since it was a small town and we were close to my house it would be okay.

Well, the guy starts talking to himself as if he's in an argument over whether or not to do something, but I can't make out anything he's saying. I can also tell we aren't going the fastest, most direct way to my house, but I don't say anything. I just kind of sit there paralyzed and hope everything is going to be okay.

After about ten minutes of riding in silence listening to this guy argue with himself, he pulls over on the side of the road. It's pouring out and we're in some other part of town, probably just as far from my house as I was when he picked me up. He told me to get out and then he looks at me and says very sternly, "Don't you ever accept a ride from a stranger again."

90

They Thought We Saw Them

One night I got home late from a work party with my wife. We actually pulled into the driveway before my wife realized she left her purse at the event, so we returned to collect her things. When we got home for good about an hour later, we discovered that someone had broken in through the back door. We called the police and they searched the house but didn't find anyone and nothing was missing.

The next day the police stopped by again. This time, they told us that a couple had broken into a neighbor's home and held them hostage for a few hours while they robbed the house. They thought that our house may have been the original target, but the robbers were spooked by us pulling into the driveway and immediately leaving.

91

Dark-Haired Woman

I grew up in the suburbs so I'd never lived in an older house before the one I bought with my wife. She grew up in a farmhouse and *loved* all the "character" the house had. I liked that it had an extra bedroom we could use for an office and that it was on the lower end of our budget.

After we moved in I found the house a bit creepy at night, but I realized I was just unfamiliar with the creaks and "settling" of an older property and I told myself I'd get used to it. I also started having dreams about a young woman with long dark hair. Her skin was pale and sallow and her expression sad. She always seemed like she wanted urgently to tell me something, but she also never spoke.

Eventually, I started seeing the woman when I was awake, but only out of the corner of my eye. When I moved my head to look, she was never there.

One weekend I met the next door neighbor out in the yard and he made a comment about seeing me and my wife around the house (we hadn't installed blinds yet). My wife came out of the house and I introduced them and my neighbor seemed con-fused. He thought my (very blonde) wife was a brunette but assumed it must just have looked that way through the window in the dark.

A few years later we had a baby shower for my sister-in-law. Some of the family brought their kids and they were running around playing games with each other throughout the event. At one point my wife's six-year-old niece starts screaming bloody murder from one of the upstairs bedrooms. She ran down the stairs and into her mother's arms, telling her that a "lady with long black hair" wouldn't leave her alone.

At that point, my wife agreed that if we could sell the house and get our money back we should move, and we were eventu-ally able to find another older house that didn't have the same creepy feel to it. I never got the impression that the dark-haired woman was evil, but I also didn't want to wait around and find out.

92

Shadow Person

I woke up one night and it felt like someone had woken me up but I was alone in my bedroom. I looked around and gradually started to see something that was a cross between a shadow and an actual person. They had the outline of a human, but they didn't seem solid. As my eyes adjusted the edges around this "person" became sharper, but it didn't move. I was so tired that I wasn't actually that scared, more just confused about what was happening.

I spent maybe five minutes watching this thing crawl across my walls with mild curiosity before I dozed off again.

When I woke up in the morning I thought I had dreamed the whole thing until I went downstairs to eat breakfast and my little brother was telling my mom about the "shadow man" who came to play in her room with her last night.

93

Easter Bunny from Hell

One year when I was in elementary school I happened to wake up the night before Easter Sunday. I was bored so I walked over to my window and peeked out. I saw the Easter Bunny hopping through the yard. It was an adult person in an Easter Bunny costume, but at the time I just thought "Easter Bunny!" I got really excited and left my bedroom and started going down the stairs, but as I walked past my parents' bedroom they stopped and asked me what I was doing. They wouldn't let me go outside and play with the Easter Bunny which made me really angry, but eventually, they got me back in bed and I went to sleep.

It wasn't until years later that I realized how creepy the whole thing was. There was some stranger outside dressed up like an Easter bunny in the middle of the night and I almost left my house to go play with them. If my parents hadn't caught me going down the stairs, they wouldn't have even noticed I was gone until morning…

94

It Wasn't Empty

When I was a kid I was playing soccer in a friends backyard when I accidentally kicked the ball over the fence. I wanted to show off so I insisted I was brave enough to reach over and unlatch the gate and let myself into the neighbor's backyard. This was in the middle of the day in the summer, so I didn't expect to see anyone.

I ran quickly to the far corner of the yard to retrieve the ball and when I turned back toward the house I saw a woman looking out the back window who looked really angry with me. I yelled out "sorry" and ran as fast as I could back to my friends. Later I was eating dinner with my family and I made a joke about how the neighbor was angry that I'd been in their yard retrieving our soccer ball and the whole family looked confused. It turns out the old lady who lived there had died earlier in the summer and her daughter hadn't gotten around to putting it on the market yet, so it was just empty.

95

Late Night Drive

My boyfriend and I were driving home from his parents' house, about a four-hour trip back to our city. It was a foggy night and the roads had a bit of an eerie quality to them. We got to a section close to his parents' town where there's a small bridge over a stream in the middle of some farmland. He was driving really slowly because the fog was especially bad around the bridge due to the water. Suddenly, we heard a loud banging sound and he slammed on the breaks. We were stopped for a few seconds when we heard the sound again and saw an old man pounding his fists on the trunk of the car. He had a cruel look on his face like he was really angry with us for being there. My boyfriend peeled out and we looked back to be like, "WTF was that?" but the guy was totally gone. To this day I don't know if he disappeared into the fog or if it was some kind of ghost.

96

He Didn't Choose Me

A weird thing happened to my group of friends in high school where we all were having dreams about this "shadow man" around the same time and he would only visit one of us a night. No two people had a dream about him on the same night, but we were all having regular dreams about him. The shadow man gave off the vibe of an adult who was trying to be cool and blend in with a kid. He'd ask us questions and then get angry and then try to buddy up to us again. For each one of us, the last dream we can recall having of him was one where he said: "Not you."

We thought it was cool and talked about it a lot but I assume most of us actually thought we were kind of egging each other on in some psychosomatic process and we grew out of it eventually.

It wasn't until I was reading the town paper a good decade later that I felt the shadow man was something sinister. A terrible thing had happened in my hometown where a boy from the high school had murdered his parents. The article I was reading in the paper had come out about a year after he'd been sentenced, it was a jailhouse interview the kid had granted to help the town understand why he did it.

In the interview, the boy talked about bad dreams. He said he dreamed about a man made of shadows who was a friend at first, but at some point, the dreams turned sinister and the man had instructed him to kill his parents over and over, every night until the kid snapped. I don't know if it's a total coincidence, but my theory is that the shadow man is some sort of demon, and he's spent years looking for the right kid until he found someone he could break down, someone he could convince to do something evil.

97

"The People with the Teeth"

I'm a hospice nurse so I have had a lot of unexplained things happen with patients, but most of them are more comforting than scary. A few times a patient has described the last patient I had in that room (who was now deceased) and said they were friendly, there to support and help. That made me feel good. If there were spirits I would love to think of my former patients successfully passing on and coming back to help others. I've also had a number of people describe seeing a tunnel of light or tell me they saw angels or relatives that had already passed on.

I've only had one patient really frighten me. He was an old man without any family which meant I paid particular attention to him, wanting him to feel comfortable and as peaceful as possible as he made his transition. He was fairly stoic and quiet which wasn't abnormal. One night it looked like he might go, but he ended up pulling through, although it was likely he only had another day or two.

His behavior changed suddenly, which also wasn't completely

unusual, but this was one of the first times I'd seen someone genuinely in a state of terror after having been there for some time already. Through the day he'd ask if I could see "them." When I asked who he was talking about he just replied "the people with the teeth." I asked him if he'd like a visit from a pastor or priest (something he'd refused previously) and he asked me to get him a priest to make a confession.

I got the priest and settled them in and then gave them some privacy. About an hour later the priest came out and seemed a big shaken up, frankly. I went back into the room and asked the patient if he needed anything. He told me he wanted to be alone, so I left him until his vitals started going down later in the night. I was in there with another nurse when the man grabbed my hand and started sobbing. "It's too late," he told me looking as sad as I've ever seen someone look. He passed that night.

People ask me about my job because they think it must be so terrible, but honestly, I get a lot of satisfaction from helping patients and their families find comfort and peace, and it usually happens like that. This one man, though…I get shaken up just thinking about him.

98

A Message

On a road trip with my girlfriend, I realized I was too tired to keep driving and I ended up pulling off the road so we could nap for a few hours before going the rest of the way.

I dozed off and woke up a bit later to a scratching sound coming from what seemed like the trunk area of the car. My girlfriend woke up and asked me what I was doing and then her eyes got really wide—she heard the scratching too. I whispered to her that it was probably a wild animal, but I wasn't convinced. The scratching sounded more intentional (as if it was meant to scare us) than an animal trying to figure out if a hunk of the car was edible.

We sat there for a few minutes praying that the noise would just go away and then decided, "Fuck it," and start the car up. We didn't need to sit there and be scared. As we drove away we both looked at the car to see if anything unusual was back there, but we just saw an empty road. We got to our destination and parked the car in a hotel parking lot. We got out of the car and went to the trunk to grab our bags when we saw someone had keyed "I can see you" into the paint on the trunk.

99

Mamabear

Growing up I had a nanny who wasn't there. She was a kindly old lady I called "Mamabear" because she was a sturdy Norwegian grandma who I thought was cuddly like a "mama bear" would be. She lived in our house and read me stories every night and would tuck me in again if I had to get up to go to the bathroom in the middle of the night. We played in the yard together, had tea parties, and sang songs we made up ourselves. She was my favorite adult and she always made me feel safe and happy. Sometimes I had other babysitters, or my real grandparents would take care of me while my parents were gone, but Mamabear was always there too.

When I was in first grade Mamabear told me that she was going to go away because I was a big kid now and I didn't need her anymore. I cried and cried but she told me she would always love me and that she would always be there even if I couldn't see her anymore. She did leave and I was very sad, but I was also a kid so eventually, I moved on.

It wasn't until high school when my parents and I were talking about growing up and I mentioned Mamabear that I realized she wasn't "real". My parents actually thought I was kidding when I insisted she was my first nanny and that she lived in the house with us. They told me "we've never had a nanny that lived in the house, we don't even have a bedroom for someone else to live in" which of course, I realized was true but it had never occurred to me before. This whole time they assumed Mamabear was an imaginary friend, and I assumed she was real.

Spookhousing

There was a long tradition in the rural farming community I grew up in of "spookhousing" which basically meant that it was a known practice that kids would explore old farm houses and grain elevators and the like pretty much because there was nothing else to do for fun. It was always an entertaining mission where you'd basically see who would get scared and run back to the car first. No one ever saw anything that scary, even though there were lots of stories about different houses and what happened to a "friend of a friend" there.

One night I was at one with a couple friends. We had mag lights and were kind of just looking through the house. I spotted a mason jar on the floor and so no one would trip on it I picked it up and set it down on a counter. For some reason, I had a really uneasy feeling at that moment and I looked up and my friends were all making eye contact with me as if they had a similar feeling.

Suddenly the mason jar I'd set on the counter flew against the wall and shattered with an extremely loud 'crack'. I honestly don't remember running out of the house because it was such a blur of adrenaline and scrambling to get through the door. We peeled out of there and I never went spookhousing again even though everyone who wasn't there thinks the story is made up.

The Hearse Driver

For as long as I can remember, I've dreamed of a big black hearse and a creepy driver with rotting teeth and gray hair. It's not something I even paid much attention to—just noticed it was something I had dreamed about before and then dismissed it as a nightmare. In the dream, the guy would park the hearse across the street from me, get out, and then open the passenger door as if he expected me to ride shotgun with him.

One day I was going to the train station and had already purchased a ticket to go to New York and visit my brother for the weekend. I was super excited about a weekend in the city and I made sure I had plenty of time to get there on time so I wouldn't miss the train. But when I got there and was about to cross the street I noticed a big black hearse parked in front of the train station, just like the one in my dream. I looked around and no one else seemed to be paying attention to the vehicle, but I just kind of stood there in shock. I take a few steps forward to get a look at the driver and sure enough, it's the creepy dude from my dream. He makes eye contact with and grins and I can see his nasty brown and yellow teeth.

I feel super freaked out and uneasy in that moment. I speed walk away from the guy and go to the station and sit down but I end up deciding not to go to New York that weekend. I didn't even think something bad would happen if I did, I was just freaked out and wanted to be at home in my own space. I called my brother and told him I wasn't feeling well and I was just going to eat the cost of my train ticket. He sounded disappointed but understood.

An hour and a half later I'm at home trying to shake off the weird feeling when my brother calls me frantically, wanting to make sure I was okay. The train I was meant to take to New York derailed and there were casualties.

About the Author

Lane Loomis is a horror writer. One day she'll write the kind of YA horror books that ruin childhoods.

Made in United States
Orlando, FL
07 February 2024

43416393R00136